'Powerful, physical, ... nostalgia and memory and the stories ... and *of* ourselves. Breathless, urgent, witty, ominous, beautiful. There are so many words I could use to describe this debut, but if I had to go with one, it would simply be *remarkable*.'

Alexander Gordon Smith

'Have you had a friend who was bewitching and unscrupulous, where the balance of need was unequal and afterwards you can't be quite sure who you were and why you needed someone who become so toxic? Be warned, Stella Bech's effortless mastery will bring that person right back. In technicolour'

Sarah Passingham, author of *Push: My Father, Polio, and Me*

'Pensive but pacey, poignant but warm, a tantalising tale about unravelling friendships wonderfully articulated.'

Ashley Hickson-Lovence, author of *The 392*

'Stella Bech describes with throbbing intensity the passion and cruelty of adolescent female friendships. Shame, betrayal, loss and the struggle for identity are portrayed with such visceral truth that the hairs on my forearms prickled and my mouth went dry.'

Sally-Anne Lomas, author of *Live Like Your Head's On Fire*

Madeleine

Stella Bech

**Story
Machine**

Madeleine, Copyright © Stella Bech, 2021

Print ISBN: 9781912665068
Ebook ISBN: 9781912665075
Published by Story Machine, 130 Silver Road, Norwich,
NR3 4TG; www.storymachines.co.uk

Set in Garamond; used under licence.

Printed and bound in the UK by Seacourt Ltd.

Story Machine is committed to the environment.
This book is printed using processes that are:

carbon positive | EMAS | renewable energy | ISO14001 | eco-friendly simitri® toner | recycled FSC® stock | Zero % waste to landfill

Printed by **seacourt** – proud to be counted amongst the top environmental printers in the world

Madeleine

Esther sent me a link just as I was going to bed.

Three girls of no more than twelve or thirteen years old formed a triangle. They took turns to come forward to outdo one another - the two behind cheering the one in front. The music was ours - the songs we'd used, years before. I watched a few videos and when I stopped to call her, I realised I was holding my breath.

'I know,' she laughed, 'and they're so much younger than we were. Can you imagine, if we'd had the internet?'

'I can't. It was traumatic enough as it was.'

'We were never that good.'

I was defensive - of all three of us. 'I don't know, we were pretty great. We had heart like these three - for a while.'

'You know I saw Madeleine a few weeks ago? She ignored me, of course, like I was a ghost. Less substantial than that, even. But I know she saw me.'

Esther hadn't mentioned it at the time.

'Are you sure it was her?'

'Yes! You've forgotten how she is - she's exactly the same now.'

I laughed then, but it wasn't funny. 'She might have been worried about what you'd say.' The sound of Madeleine's name from Esther's mouth had planted something in me, a tightness that started in my gut and travelled upwards.

'Oh no I doubt that. I probably just didn't fit, with whatever her idea of herself is now. I'm sure none of it's that conscious.'

We didn't talk for long. Esther was on her way to work in London, and it was late here. Unable to recover the present, I watched more videos. The whole operation was stronger than ours. It looked like there was money behind it: parents, management. But I knew how they felt. The adrenaline, the power, the compulsive danger of being so young, and good, and on the brink.

What kept me awake was Madeleine and the feeling she seemed to pull from me. A remorse that was almost maternal. I was surprised how rattled Esther was by the encounter with her, in ways she must have been years ago, too. Esther and I rarely talked about Madeleine - not then and not later either. But she was there, still. As I went over it, picturing the two women passing in the street in a country that used to be mine, something else reached me from miles and years away. It left again almost instantly, but for a second there it was like a pushed bruise. The old sensation of being nowhere near enough.

◆

I can never remember meeting Madeleine, which is both odd, and, when I think about it, not at all.

The story has to start further back.

◆

The headmistress of Glendale school threatens you when you say you want to leave. 'You *will fail.*' It is 1996. You are sixteen. Mrs Abram wears floral dresses draped across her large, oblong frame. Her head - always visible due to her height - stalks the school like a silverback gorilla's - close-shaven, masculine, thuggish. Girls had to make an appointment to say it to her face: *I want to leave.* And it was unusual. You were on track for the best education there was. Esther said her meeting had been fine.

You can't think of a response to what is a threat rather than a question, and her pedantic country accent seems to sew things up, so you grimace a dumb mixture of archness and shock and leave the meeting unsure if your resignation has even been accepted. The answer you'd rehearsed, that you and Esther discuss all the time - that you want to live in the real world as part of your education, *with actual people of the opposite sex* - had seemed too ridiculous to say in the room.

At the open evening the New School was so 'new' it

was a disaster zone-like collection of leaking portacabins standing in for the collapsing tower of the main building - and it terrified you. Your real reason - that you must go because Esther is going; because you believe no-one can like you, and that all these sheltered little girls you've written off have hurt you; you want another chance - is too pathetic to admit to yourself.

In your final report Mrs Abram writes a personal note, which you read like a criminal. 'Angela has been a wonderful student in every respect - a very special girl. We wish her every success and happiness.'

Had you been wonderful? *Were you,* special? A scholarship student, making up the numbers - and now bringing them down. So ungrateful. You feel sometimes ancient (like you've done things before, a million times), sometimes superhuman with possibility. But surrounding this, like a radioactive organ, throb billowing layers of blinding shame. You piece together identity from clues and fragments other people drop; shards of a broken mirror you bend to gather, furtive, after the event. At a party one of the boys says: 'You could have anyone here, you know that don't you?'

And yet nothing ever happens. You've never kissed anyone, never had a boyfriend. Only an idea that maybe after all this time trying to escape your age, you've overshot the mark - so that now you're older than all of them, untouchable - *post-sexual!*

'You can come off arrogant,' your sister once told you. 'It's your face. So you have to make extra effort, you know?'

The effort is gratifying to other people, like a party trick - *Oh my god Angie, she's smart, but so dumb!!* You watch as much as you can, developing a second sight, a third, hundreds, so that you can watch yourself at any moment in multicam. On the bus, listening to music and seeing the film of yourself as you perform it. Walking down the street, hearing catcalls and whistles a second before they come, like a sixth sense. The almost unbearable experience of walking into any full room, with its dozens of eyes.

◆

You have realised: if you don't make things happen, they won't - or they might, but in a way that is worse. Further back. 1994. You are fourteen. Your sister introduces you to a clothes shop. The owners are friendly, it's a way to practise flirting, look around, maybe buy something when you have money; she always has it under control. But then one time when you go in alone, Andy, a man in his thirties who has more than once flipped open his wallet to show you the picture of his kids, comes round the counter, and checking over your shoulder to see he has the shop to himself pushes his tongue into your mouth. It's repulsive, but there's satisfaction chasing the disgust - the old deadening triumph of a boundary broken, the recounting already forming in your mind - and as he pulls away to look at you, you feel your mouth work to say, 'But you're married!'

He laughs at that, as if you're speaking different languages - or as people laugh at their child learning words. You can't understand how he could do what he's doing - even as you realise the protest you actually verbalised is a kind of cop-out - a line from a soap opera. *Angie, Angie, Angie,* he says, like a nursery rhyme. He is small, shorter than you by four inches. You can see the baby in his face.

◆

At Glendale, you have to do 'work experience' for a week. It is 1995. You are fifteen. Your father arranges this for you with a professional acquaintance; a documentary filmmaker doing odd-jobs between projects - driving from place to place in his tinny old Ford Fiesta, covering local news. He is small, almost frail, with a yellow-grey creeping beard that looks like it has never been cut, it just ends like a wisp of smoke half way down his chest. He suggests your movements hesitantly all week:

'Shall we go here? Do you want to stand here?'

It is excruciating, but in a way that's so familiar it's ordinary - to feel your own skin trying to crawl off your body as you work out how to be. At the end of the week, in the relief of sitting next to him for the last time in his car, as you fix your eyes on the dusty air filters on the dashboard, he blurts: 'It's a miracle! You're lucky I haven't molested you, I've had to stop myself all week!'

You walk away, seeing yourself from behind with his eyes, in your tight-fitting leggings and top that had felt so - what, Angela? Sophisticated? *Competent?* - and which now feel like wearing your own labia. You call your mother from the nearest phone box, your only idea being to enrage her sympathy. But maybe there was a question. Maybe because of what happened to her you are both cursed. The more it happens, the more people see it in you; they do it again. On the phone she sounds tired and is angry, dismissive ('Yes, well, sometimes men are like that!') - your naivety offends her. Worse than that, it's a kind of assault in itself. How could you ever compete? *How could you try?* Sometimes you are such a dumb bitch.

Your mother, too familiar, like an old skin. Your sisters suffocating and high-definition. Esther. They are all people sure enough for you to dissolve your agency around, so you can exist *with* them, as an adjunct. It pleases you to relinquish decisions, ideas about what to do, how to spend time. You have no confidence about those things on your own, interrogating each moment, relentless: *Is this the right way to do it? Is this fun? Is this what I want?* It is only possible to live through others, to feel their enjoyment. You don't know how to do it yourself. Esther, whose American father gives pep talks, tells you something he says to her:

'He calls it the honey in your soul. It's like: you know there's something good there - that you can always rely on.'

At the same time as trying and failing to imagine your own father saying anything like this, you know what she means. Esther *is* special, and sometimes so are you. But you are also not special. You are also a void. Anti-matter.

◆

One of the earliest memories: it is 1996; your seventeenth birthday, Maddie gives you a postcard - a blue line drawing of a female figure. As a child, when the question was asked and answered all the time, you always said your favourite colour was blue (navy) - but Madeleine doesn't know that. On the back, in the incongruous, sloping handwriting of an old woman, the still sixteen year-old Maddie has written, 'Dear Angie, You're a wonderful person. Happy birthday! Love, M.'

Sentimental declarations have been quite commonplace among your friends - with all the endings and beginnings of teen-age - but on the other hand you and Madeleine have known each other for three weeks. So this becomes the first marker - the first real impression is this card, and sitting opposite Maddie with her bare face open and composed as she watches you respond, on the bus to school.

◆

It's not just meeting Maddie that you don't remember. Instead of a sequence of events, your first term at the New School merges into a kaleidoscope of impressions that you store for much later. On the first day as you stand in line, in a cold rush it comes to you what will be different and what will not. A chance to be new, with people who don't know your old story; all of them drawn like instant family to Esther, but uneasy around you - your old story is not the problem. At first, Madeleine is just one of these people.

Maddie finds Esther (who she shares two classes with) first - of course - and then you. Maddie knows some people who came from her previous school, but she doesn't have an old friendship like yours with Esther. When you meet, she's from a different tribe - she looks like an art student in her witchy, homemade contraptions of figure-hugging draped black jersey. Within weeks she's looking more like you and Esther - leggings or jeans, and massive trainers - and you go clothes shopping together, hunting and celebrating second-hand treasures.

Later, you have a catalogue of these gentle impressions of Madeleine. Maddie, with a near-constant laugh in her voice. The way Maddie introduces herself, with a big smile, wrapping her mouth around the word as if it were a fruit, the act of saying it a joy itself: 'Madeleine'. Maddie's wide, open face that contained something - a confrontation? - a plainness and a sophistication - exposed and obscure - and her sleek brown-black hair. So different to you, and so familiar. Maddie, expecting to be loved. The surprising quality of her laugh when it comes: guttural, raucous, bursting from her statuesque body. Maddie, always making plans - *What's happening at the weekend? Are you going? Have you got tickets yet? Do you want to stay at mine?* Maddie, dancing to nothing, as she stands in conversation, creating an audience from nowhere. In the school courtyard between classes, smoking in groups. Waving to each other over other people's heads.

At the end of the first term everyone goes to watch the dance students' first performance. It's a contemporary piece, everyone dressed in white. You retain almost nothing of it, save some images of Maddie; committed, always central, being carried across the pitted parquet floor in the glare of cheap stage lights on the others' shoulders, radiant.

But these memories come much later (you polish them

into existence, like Gollum). The first term - the first year, even - of knowing Maddie, seems unremarkable as you live it. You don't tell yourself: *this is it.*

◆

You and your mother were rehoused a couple of years before, to an estate on the edge of town. Somewhere in those years with your sisters both gone, blame and doubt multiplied between the two of you in such prolific mirroring neither of you knew where to turn but away. And now you do everything you can to get back to where school and everything else is, in the city. You try not to spend more than one night in one place (you can't run out of welcome), so you sleep a night at your sister's, a night at Esther's or another friend's, and - more and more - at Maddie's.

When you stay at her flat, or when Madeleine talks to any of you about her life outside school, you are continually faced with her maturity. Maddie lends the plainest tasks sophistication. The way she conducts her relationships, with men - *men!* - outside school - and the way the status of these relationships is never clear. The way she lives alone on an allowance from her mother, who is absent - and, you gather, unwell - bar the money which she sends in bundles of cash. Her woman's body, when you still feel like a child with new parts someone has stuck on to your eleven year-old's figure. The way she talks to the man at the shop on her corner as if she's fifty and they go back decades. The way she cooks pasta for anyone who turns up on a weeknight, and more elaborate meals at weekends. Her restraint and conscientiousness when it comes to school. The way her only vice now is cigarettes, but she's always giving up (and is far less tied to smoking than you; you *need* the prop, you *enjoy* the gentle self-harm of a singed throat and fingers) having renounced her earlier, debauched years already. Maddie has a past - who else of you, beyond infancy and puberty, can say that? - which she refers to but never in detail. She has turned her life around, probably at great cost, which she never dwells on, but there it is: her past, behind her. Maddie's enormous brown eyes are bloodshot, and they seem older by years than the rest of her body. And now on the other side there is something pure about her, she is a *new leaf.* Maddie has learned her life lessons already, and is doing things the right way. You find this comforting. It curbs your wilder spasms, and you assume Maddie has learned for both of you. You don't need to stay out all night doing hard drugs, because Maddie's done it. It's okay to stay in and eat pasta at Maddie's - in fact, it is the most glamorous option. Going out with Maddie, on the other hand, is the most fun. She knows where to go, how to get there, how to dance together - in a circle that excludes everyone else - who to talk to, who to ignore, when to leave.

◆

It is 1997. You are seventeen. At a club you meet a guy who says he works in music A&R, twenty years older than you. He's not attractive but he persists. He claims a kind of celibacy that becomes an unfunny joke between you - making you anxious you will, in fact, *never* ' lose your virginity' - but you stay at his flat, and he fetishises your mouth; each kiss, he says, is a delicacy. He tells you at length about his 'dilemma' over you and another girl, Keisha, who he also met at the club. He tells you what his mother says to him: that both girls are sent by the devil to test him; that neither of you *really cares* about him. You keep going back because you're researching, because you have to have something to do when Madeleine and Esther are with their boyfriends, because you can't remain asexual. One day, when you drop by to see him at work, he takes you into a storeroom where you almost have sex, but instead he sticks his big dry thumb roughly inside you, laughing at your confusion as at a practical joke (which maybe it is).

In the spring of the first year at school, you move into the spare room at your sister's house in the city. You work two jobs to cover your contribution to the bills, one at a call centre in the evenings, and a Saturday job at a book shop nearby.

You give up on the music guy, chasing down a beautiful boy in the year above at school, who's leaving soon. Next to the wall you've covered in old photographs (Angie as a toddler! Angie as a seven year-old! Angie with her friends!) and flyers, you watch the fine gold chain he wears, rocking with him over you, hanging just below his chin and sometimes catching on it. The next morning as he sleeps, you soak your butchered muscles in a bath, telling your sister all about it. You're concerned - though not much - that he didn't buy your lie that you'd started your period, to explain the blood as he battled his way inside. You are exhilarated: it is done. And worth it for the story to take to Maddie and Esther.

The three of you start spending time at a recording studio in the city run by a woman called Jenna, a new friend of Esther's. You never know who you might see there - sometimes no-one for a whole day, in which case all the more time for talking, smoking, making tea. It's not that you like Jenna, exactly, but she can talk to anyone - and she knows something about everyone. She collects keys and capital in the form of knowledge about people - she has apparently always been there, watching, recording, collecting anecdotes and pieces of gossip. She combines a prurient interest in all three of you with enough emotional intelligence and passivity to make you feel at ease exposing the most intimate actions and feelings - Jenna portrays herself as a hopeless romantic, destined to pine for oblivious and out-of-reach women - or girls. She is always falling in unrequited love with someone. That's how she meets you, when Esther becomes the object of her latest crush.

◆

You start skipping classes, working for free at the front desk at Jenna's. It's not really work, she doesn't need anyone on the desk most of the time but you want to be there and she wants you to be there, and it just about dignifies that. You start using one of the studios to put together dance routines with Maddie and Esther. They both take dance at school and you don't, but you're in charge. It is different for you, you think. Your grandmother was a dancer, and she would never have done 'A Level dance,' so neither do you. You study video tapes: Missy Elliott, Madonna, Michael Jackson, old Jack Cole and Berry Brothers choreography, trying to recreate steps and come up with your own and it's the most fun you've ever had, working out sequences with the girls, seeing it work out; seeing people see you; thrilling them. Jenna thinks you have potential, and so do the musicians she brings by so she can show you off (they - all of them men except the odd female vocalist - start referring to you as The Girls, with an intimidated quality to their tone which is only half-joking). You can see Jenna enjoys the idea of being an agent with ingenues. She takes it on as a kind of mission to find you gigs. She says you're doing something new, and that clubs will pay good money for your act. You are sick with excitement when you think of what you might do.

You tell Jenna a lot. She glamorises everything through her audienceship. 'I cry most days,' you tell her to provoke her to chide you to expect more - more happiness. It isn't true - you don't cry most days, but you are sad in a way that feels out of control and that you don't communicate to anyone else, and you want her to think of you as romantic, complex, special. It's interesting to see what you can get. She says to you things like, 'The amazing thing about you - I was talking about this with Estie - is you have no idea how *beautiful* you are!' But sometimes you do know. They are your secrets, that you can see every day, in the mirror; how beautiful you can be, how ugly you are. Your reflected image has been a consolation and a disturbance for as long as you can remember - even as a small child: *This is me!,* you'd think, with a kind of wonder at being in existence at all. But any satisfaction is temporary, vaporous. Inside and underneath, what's really there is rotten, unconnected to the outside and a constant threat: at any point the ugliness could come out. (People see it, you think; they are the ones who don't say anything.) So you cover it. And when someone says something good, you hide your feral hunger for the fleeting reprieve.

◆

The guy Maddie sees most is a neighbour five doors down from her flat. He's got a wife and two kids, and he takes Maddie shopping for clothes. Maddie disappears to see him, sometimes for a couple of days. She doesn't speak about him much - he is a blank in your mind, out of scope just as your parents are. You saw him once and he looked nice, older, good looking but cleancut, with glasses, like a great guy and a great dad who would never cheat. She says, 'I've got to see Michael tonight - he thinks I've been neglecting him!' It's a perspective that must keep both Michael and you happy at once - it is mostly *you* depriving Michael of Maddie - and you take it as a compliment - even as you're deprived of Maddie's company for a day or two.

Something happens to the lines between you and Maddie. One day in the courtyard at school, a friend of yours (who Maddie always ignores) gets up from the steps where the two of you have been sitting and smoking and says to you, 'You realise I've been sitting right next to you for *fifteen minutes?'* He's aghast, and you and Madeleine just laugh. Of course you haven't noticed. You are delighted with your own bad manners, because it's proof of your love. Madeleine's brightness, her connection with the present at the expense of the past, acts as an effacement of a certain kind of thought, so that it's impossible for you to reflect on your relationship. Why would you, when it is so full, so present, so pressing? If you had had to describe Maddie, or why you liked her - as you later try - what could you have said? Not that you have interests in common, or that Madeleine's character has similar vibrations or tendencies to yours - or even ones you admire. It is something else. Where you are deficient, Madeleine compensates; where you long, Madeleine requites; where you've never had a grasp on affection, Madeleine suggests devotion as if it is simple, automatic; where you recoil from yourself, Madeleine shines uncritical, bleaching sunshine on both of you; where your mind and love are shaped around and towards the regaining of something lost, Maddie is there, laughing, to be found.

On the way home from school after the bus, there's a shortcut to Maddie's place - a hundred or so winding steps to one of the highest points of the city. As with everything at this time it becomes a joke between you - by the time you reach the top, you will both be hysterical with laughter. It's a law of your own, of the two of you - if you and Maddie have enough time together, this is the result. The delight in each other is guaranteed and constantly renewing. With Madeleine you are funny, beautiful, clever, always wanted. Maddie is Maddie: plain and fascinating, simple and not, young and old, familiar and alien, platonic and devoted, unknowable and available. It's not clear what Madeleine's ideas are, but it is clear to you she understands and appreciates yours, as if they've come from Maddie herself.

◆

You spend more time at Jenna's over the summer and into your final school year, turning up for classes less. She gets you a trial gig at your favourite club, in the 10pm-1am slot on a Saturday night, and you rehearse obsessively. Esther and Madeleine both take school more seriously than you, but Madeleine often turns up at the studio at the end of the afternoon, where you've been rehearsing and sourcing music for hours. She's greeted by you and Jenna like you've all just won something, as she floods you all with kinetic joy; grinning, excited, ready with a joke or anecdote, always on the edge of laughter.

In the autumn term Maddie decides to split up with Michael. It comes out of nowhere, and you haven't even thought it was the kind of relationship that required 'breaking up', but when she says it to you, it seems inevitable. 'It's time for me to be who I am, to live my life, not be tied to someone older.' She knows what she's doing. And more of Maddie can only be a good thing. You double down on rehearsals, which means even more time at Jenna's getting ready for Christmas. It's a big time for the promoter and if it goes well she thinks you'll be offered a residency.

A couple of days into the new year, you spend a quiet

day of the holiday together, at Maddie's. It is 1998. You are eighteen. After sleeping late and watching a film after lunch, you try on clothes and talk through some new ideas for the act. Madeleine asks you to put makeup on her, just to try it, as she never uses any, preferring to keep her face plain. So you do it the way you do your own face: two thick lines of black on the eyes, pencil around the lips. As you do it, you think of how you are drawing the features as if they won't be there otherwise, and it is suddenly ludicrous. Maddie cackles at herself in the mirror delighted, and says she looks dead, that her mother told her makeup didn't suit her - her lips are big enough already. It is true: the things you rely on for yourself make Maddie look strange. Her wide mouth is too much, and looks older somehow; obscene. It makes the memory of her usual, un-made-up face more beautiful to you, and it makes your attempts at making your own face up feel ridiculous. Maddie doesn't need it, but for you it's essential disguise, and also definition: what would be there without? There is something in the attention you both give Maddie that's disturbing, but it's such an unwelcome perception - and so small - that you can bury it inside a gentle nausea. After taking off the makeup, you decide to go out to eat. You walk across town to the Spanish place, sitting across from each other, surrounded by couples and joking that it's like a date. You don't know; *you still don't know it,* but it is all you want, to be with her - and it's already all you have left.

◆

You and Jenna have shifted from talking with Maddie as a three, to talking about her when she's not there. Jenna announces later this same week, with a slavering grin, that she is 'in love' with Maddie. (It seems one of the great pleasures of falling in love with Maddie, is to confess it to you). You tell her about your Mona Lisa Theory of Maddie: only some people can see, you say, her beauty - which is her spirit - others just see plainness, or nothing. And it's a kind of trick to catch it - to see the power of this strange and simple face. As if you've said nothing, Jenna says, 'It's amazing! I didn't really see it coming.' And, as if she's in love with the paradox itself - and herself for pulling it off - 'it's not like there's anything spectacular about Maddie - you're much better looking - and she's not as interesting, or funny, or smart as Esther - I mean Wesley can't *stand* her. I think she's a bit Marmite - you either get it or you don't. But it's crept up on me. She's just gorgeous, and she's so *full of herself.*'

You tell Maddie about it later that day at her place. She's cooking while you sit on the kitchen step looking at a photograph her mother must have taken: Maddie at four years old, sitting unstable on top of a climbing frame, gawky legs bent at one angle, body the other, for balance; wind blowing long strands of black hair wildly across her face; and the even wilder ecstatic smile you know, right into the camera. You have a momentary fantasy - almost a hallucination - of being Maddie's mother, looking at it. You have never seen anything sweeter. You find yourself thinking of Maddie's father, who, like yours, had left by the time she was two years old. *How could anyone leave that?,* you think, as you tell a blasé, laughing Maddie about Jenna's big confession. Maddie takes it in her stride - something to be expected: 'Hahah! My aunt says everyone falls in love with me!' A tug in your brain, away from the photo; the slightest twist of self-awareness, like an alarm - but it's bodily and you shake it off.

◆

At New Year's Eve Madeleine had given her number to Noah (another older man, but only twelve years this time), an actor - who you all thought you recognised - home for the holidays. A couple of weeks later, Maddie plays her anticipation of their first date down. In her bedroom, you watch while she changes, into tight trousers, new trainers, and a black fake fur coat you've never seen before. 'How do I look?' she asks, twirling around and flashing her eyes at you - and you're unclear whether she knows she's a cliché or not, but neither option can dampen the effect - she looks five years older, beautiful, different. Like the girlfriend of a famous actor. *How does she know how to do that?* Noah comes to pick Maddie up in his car; you hear his horn from the street outside, Maddie skips down the stairs and calls behind her for you to let yourself out whenever. You leave shortly after, realising you have no plans, and will have to consider this other Madeleine, until you can talk again.

◆

For a while, Maddie's relationship with Noah doesn't change things much. He's either out of work or putting it aside for Maddie, but he stays in town for weeks. They go for dinner dates and drinks, sometimes to gigs, but she's careful to make time for you. You're clear with each other: *friends mean more than men* - and in particular, your friendship comes first. You carry on rehearsing and performing, becoming more ambitious, negotiating more pay from the promoter at the club, and trying out some gigs in different clubs. Your promoter doesn't like this, but Maddie has a way of handling him, of talking to him. You feel when they talk that you're leaving it to the adults, and you can see how he responds to Maddie, like a stroked cat - as if all her suggestions are not only reasonable, but admirable.

Esther calls you to tell you she's leaving the act. She has too much on, she says, with school work and her jobs, she can't give it what it deserves - you and Maddie are so much more dedicated. You can tell it's a hard decision - *Esther is telling you it is hard,* and she sounds upset on the phone. You also know this is one of the repercussions of your growing closeness to Maddie - of course there will be casualties! - and in a way, you've only left your old sociable friend Esther in the way Esther has so often left you - preferring others. You know all this, that you could be losing an old friend, but all you can think about is how much possibility it holds for you and Madeleine: you *have* always been more dedicated, you practise more together, care more, and it shows. It is a relief; Esther was holding you back. You go through the motions of empathy as if drawing from memory, and as soon as you get off the call from Esther, you call Maddie to make plans.

Maddie brings Noah to meet you and Esther at your favourite pub, like an interview, or a rite of passage she's just made up. 'I've told him he needs to meet you and pass the test!' she laughs. And you all enjoy it, imagining you are *giving him a run for his money, putting him through the mill*, making him justify his interest in Maddie - with the people who matter most. But you are also trying to impress and entertain him, this older, famous man. You feel the precarious altitude of your effort. You are on the line, with this person you know nothing of. When Maddie and Noah go home afterwards, and Esther goes to her boyfriend's house, the nausea swells into the old engulfing loss: you are left behind. Everything that night was in the service of Maddie's date, Maddie's impression, on Noah. You and your ideas, your capacities, your nerves, your jokes, your interest, were all just part of Maddie's. It wasn't an interview - Noah had already been accepted. It was an extended date, an advertisement for Madeleine, spectacularly orchestrated.

◆

A month later, you, Maddie and Esther plan supper and a film at Maddie's flat. When you arrive, you can hear cello playing inside, and you have to knock three times before Maddie answers the door. 'My mum sent it, it's my old one,' she explains, gesturing to the instrument lying on its side on the floor, as if impatient to get past it. You've never heard Maddie play (but you've talked about both having learned, she knows about your father - that it's his instrument). You think Maddie was trying to show you something, but you can't think what, because it's indirect, so you can't even look at it. As if you could embarrass Maddie in your own mind, just by thinking about it. So of course you don't. Maddie is in crisis. The night before, on the way to dinner with his agent, Noah stopped the car and told Maddie he'd had some mushrooms, and offered Maddie some. She had refused, outraged.

'I mean, you don't fucking do that!' she rages. 'I've *been* there, and he knows that - we've talked about how I need to focus now and I'm not interested in that any more, and he *still* thinks it's cool to drop that on me - *Hey Maddie, let's make this a bit more fun!* - right before I meet his agent?! I mean what the fuck?!' On the way home, they'd fought in the car. Noah had started laughing about a point halfway through dinner when he said Maddie's head morphed into a giant, purple octopus, and she'd lost her shit, screaming until he let her out of the car.

'Oh my *god*...Maybe, he was nervous?' you offer. You are adrenalised. Maddie is furious, but it's exciting, like a play: you haven't seen her like this before and you want to see her range - what she will do, what she will think. She might break up with him. In the end, an hour later Noah turns up, crashing your evening with endless conversation with Maddie on the building steps out front, hashing it out while you and Esther sit inside, half watching the film, eating the food Maddie has made. You are on tenterhooks, hungry for catastrophe, but by the end of the evening when Maddie comes back in, having said goodbye to Noah, it's clear nothing will change. Maddie is pale, solemn and resolute, a figure from a religious painting. She has decided to put Noah through his paces, to make it a proper crisis, but not to let him go. He has a stay, not a pardon. You're scared for Noah, but with a curious and stupid appetite, like one dog watching another get kicked: he deserves it, and Maddie is magnificent, in her unglamorous, off duty clothes, cello on the floor.

◆

Esther, still enjoying guest-list privileges, brings a guy to see your act. She's told you about meeting him earlier the same week, in a shop where he was distributing flyers. Esther describes him as a pest, bouncing around her like a dog, trying to get her attention, chatting her up, extracting information that excited him, like the fact she and her girlfriends had started this dance act, that she'd just left. She says he invaded her space, was a bit of a creep, following her to the cash machine, not letting her go, inviting himself to their night.

He's probably high, but you don't think of that, assuming his behaviour - po-going around with massive, pestering enthusiasm for you and your dancing - is him. Josh *is* like a puppy: you don't find him attractive, but he's unignorable, undeterrable, ebullient. His enthusiasm for all three of you is appealing; he is an instant one-man fan club. Hovering just offstage, he buys drinks, dances convulsively - ridiculous; stops to study your moves, toasts you loudly. *'You should come to my new night!'* he screams, as you climb down for your break, sealing your ear shut with your finger to hear his voice over the speakers. *'In fact, you should*

DANCE!' When he speaks to Maddie you see that she smiles almost in spite of herself, lips pressed a little to contain the pleasure, giving the impression she's tolerating a favourite child.

◆

Josh invites you and Maddie to the pub the following Sunday night, to plan your debut at his night. You can feel Maddie shifting around him, leaving you temporarily, in the way she does with the club promoter. But it's not a Maddie you recognise. Is she acting? Everything is the beginning of an innuendo, given to Josh, for him to enjoy completing. Dismissing a concern about how they might handle moonlighting for another new promoter, Maddie says, 'We can work it,' vibrating with satisfaction (as you sit, a superfluous witness). 'Oh, I know you can *work it,'* Josh replies, smiling as if Maddie is jerking him off under the table. When you're alone again, Madeleine is business-like about Josh, like he's a type she knows well - who needs handling. But you catch the briefest shadow of the same smile, that she's unable or unconcerned to suppress.

◆

At the start of spring your sister moves away and you have to move back home with your mother. It's the last place you want to be, but you tell yourself *it is good for you.* A good time to focus on school before final exams. You are cut off. Maddie is often with Noah, sometimes with other friends you either don't know, or don't like. And, you discover, with Josh. 'I got this with Josh the other day - it's *so dope,*' Maddie tells you, using a word you've never heard her use and pulling a new record out of her collection - and there's something off about it that you can't place. It's strange to you that they would see each other alone, without you. You would never think of going out with Josh on your own, but then, you never know how to progress friendships. Record shopping is something you and Maddie always do together, taking your grimy, fat wads of cash from the club each week on the rounds of the city's best shops, where they know you and your act and what you're looking for, setting aside piles of records. You go home to your mother's house like a child - ruminations creeping under your skin like roots; wondering over and over, what you're missing in the city, where Maddie is, what she's doing. Your whole mind, your whole experience is turned towards Maddie, as a kind of question you can't articulate to yourself.

But still, you aren't worried as much as paralysed.

◆

Over the Easter holiday your mother goes to Italy with her new boyfriend and you look forward to playing house:

smoking, playing records louder than the neighbours can take, making mixtapes, eating junk, and trying to scratch together places to stay for trips into the city - just like before. A letter comes from school addressed to your mother, and without compunction you open and read it, knowing before you do what it might contain, but not its severity. It's from the head of the school (who you've never met), and explains, briefly, that this is your final warning over attendance.

One night, when she's free, Maddie comes to stay. You make a mixtape together for Noah. You dance, and smoke, and you quiz Maddie about Noah - in the first real chance you've had since they began seeing each other intensely. You suspect Maddie is in love, but she's reticent about it in a way that doesn't tally with the facts of the relationship - the number of hours she's started to devote to him. 'I'm *into* him,' she says. 'I just, I think I'm too young to get into a massive relationship.' Jenna calls while she's there, going on and on to you about when will she see you both, when will you next come to the studio - she misses you, you aren't coming as much as you used to, you owe her money. Maddie sits across the kitchen table from you, smiling, eating nachos, unconcerned, at one point making a 'W' sign with her fingers (*'Whatever!'*), to get you to wrap up the call. The next day you take the back seat of the empty bus into the city, Maddie falling asleep with her head in your lap and feet up, her newly painted fingernails like lollipops on your leg, while you try not to move, feeling blessed and doomed.

◆

Stella Bech

Madeleine throws a dinner party bringing disparate friends together. Noah is away working. It's the first dinner party you've been to as an adult guest. You are amazed - as ever - that Maddie knows what to do. When you arrive, Josh is already there, 'helping'. Without fuss, Maddie has made lasagna and salad for ten, laid out on neighbours' borrowed tables pushed together, while keeping Josh's yapping at bay. You're still scraping the last of it from your plates, when Josh suggests a line of coke - 'for dessert!' The room quickly divides, into leavers (mostly) and takers. You watch doubt fill the eyes of Tom and Katie, two friends from school who say No at the same time as trying not to show disapproval. Maddie goes to fetch a hand mirror. You decide to try it; the work of a millisecond, not so much a decision as a shift.

'Are you sure?' Maddie asks you, as she passes the mirror, and it might have embarrassed you, were it not so quiet, so familiar, with concern. Maddie and Josh have probably been doing cocaine before you even arrived. As you take the rolled up note, an involuntary series of thoughts that are more like sensations: your mother, your sisters (who never do this and would never want you to) and your niece; of being a child in a family; your father - has he ever done this?; your old, child-self still so close; all killed off as the powder hits your brain.

◆

After that you never know if you're going to do coke or not. You don't discuss it, but sometimes it happens, sometimes it doesn't. The Maddie who worried about drugs, who'd renounced them, sometimes appears, but she's mostly gone. The new Maddie is even more accomplished, and her eyes are harder. She knows what is good cocaine and what is bad. She spends a whole night shouting at Josh once, when he brings her substandard supply. You are like her drug-child: Maddie is the one who gets the drugs, Maddie is the one who decides when you do them, and when you stop; how much you can cope with. Maddie has already felt any feeling you could have, doing cocaine, and is sympathetic and available, joking afterwards about your obnoxious talking, manic affection, and excruciating comedowns (which you experience, always, as a mental breakdown, thoughts spiralling and multiplying until it seems they come at you from somewhere else, as senseless attacks). When you stay at Maddie's, she fetches a full carton of juice from the fridge to keep by the bed, because she knows how to survive. She puts Kate Bush in the tape deck to soothe you to sleep - Maddie always sleeps, while you feel your mind fall apart during the long hours until the morning, when she wakes. When she gets up from the mattress on the floor to go to the bathroom, quietly so as not to wake you, you watch her move up and away, on legs like sculpted plaster.

◆

On your way out one night, you've run out of clean clothes, so Maddie pulls out a tiny pair of soft grey trousers that look cute on her, but are too tight for you. You feel ridiculous and exposed - in your mind you're cutting the curves off your body, which are in the wrong place, because they're not Maddie's - but she pushes your anxiety aside - 'They're fine! *Come on!!*' You walk down the steps you used to laugh your way up, the hot summer air making the trousers cling even more to the pastey blocks of dumb meat that are your thighs, it's excruciating; and Maddie starts describing sex with Noah. As with everything now to do with Maddie, you want to know - but it leaves you depleted and damaged. Last time Noah was in town they stayed at a new boutique hotel in the old quarter, and the next door room had complained about the noise. Maddie says to you, laughing, gleeful, 'There's this thing I do...He thinks I'm some kind of witch! Hahah!' You sit down on the bus stop bench that's made to be precarious, the pink sky bleeding purple and the air close around you, tortured still by these fucking trousers, and you look at Maddie, who is reckless.

Maddie says, 'Sometimes, I just do this, it's so simple, nothing really - like this,' showing you, as she talks, she kisses you once, twice, so light as to barely graze the skin of your cheek. There's a vertigo, something physical and painful that shouldn't be there, tilts and then caves inside you. Maddie laughs and turns the other way to look for the bus.

◆

In the spring, your eldest sister gets married, offering you the run of her flat for the two weeks of her honeymoon. It is a gift. Freedom, security, somewhere in the city to live, somewhere to be, to come and go from. You've made feverish plans with Maddie - you will cook, watch films, go out and come back to sleep there, knuckle down to revision for the final exams that are just around the corner. But for your first couple of nights she is with Noah, so you call Esther, who isn't in, then Josh.

He brings wine and a film. Within half an hour you are on your sister's bed, on the unfamiliar duvet with the weird pattern her boyfriend must have picked, taking off your clothes. You're in a hurry, not from desire; you're nervous as always, and impatient to kill the child - to become accomplished. It's easy to pretend it's desire. He treats you casually. Like a girl who won't mind if he flips you over within a minute. Neither of you have a condom, you don't use protection, it isn't a question between you, and only barely in your mind. Afterwards he leaps out of bed to the bathroom, to fetch snacks, to put the film on, chattering away incessantly about plans for the next forty eight hours, to stay holed up there together. You think of the tiger in the children's book, with his wide grin, assuming the house and all the things in it, part conman, part vagrant. It's easy, to be swept up in his plans even as you mock them. He wants to be with you until he doesn't. In the morning he leaves after all, he has something he remembers he has to do, but promises to call and come back to stay again that night. You didn't sleep well, waking from paranoid dreams to the strange smell of someone new in someone else's bed. You tell him you should revise anyway, and you realise you're glad. You feel a euphoria that's new to you, of being alone after being with a man. You run a bath and call Esther, who you invite over for a barbecue that night with Kim from school, already planning to blow Josh off.

Half an hour before they arrive, Josh calls. His voice sounds new, and there's a distance to it - it's the first time you've ever heard him serious, he sounds like a child attempting to be grown up. He can't or doesn't say his Rs properly, they come out as Vs - you've noticed it before, but it's suddenly ridiculous. It crosses your mind he's going to tell you someone's dead. 'I'm calling because I've got something really hard to say to you Angie. It's really hard, because I think you're great, really, an amazing girl. But…' His voice faltering, but relishing the secret - or the divulging? - like a preference of sweets, in a way that is almost camp. 'You see, I've got to be honest with you - and myself - that, I really like *Maddie.'*

You don't understand. Why is he telling you this, now? What does liking Maddie have to do with anything? Then you realise: he is telling you a decision, as something that he thinks might be damaging but necessary to hear. He is telling you he doesn't want you, when you haven't asked - and hadn't thought you cared. A tension lodges like a chicken bone in your chest as you try to respond; to make a response. Finally you wrangle something like indignation, and put it into your voice. 'What the *fuck?'* you say, sounding enraged in a way you don't expect. 'Don't you think you could have realised that *before last night*?!' You press the receiver without putting the handset down so you can call Maddie immediately, but she also sounds new, and like she knows what's coming. Heedless, without registering the withdrawal in Maddie's voice and as in a nightmare, you go through the motions of describing the night before with Josh. What he said, what he did, the phone call minutes before. It's like throwing yourself down a hill; each detail another wound you give yourself. You are asking - pleading - for understanding and advocacy. For Maddie to say, 'Oh Ange, let me come over!' But she listens without a word to the end and then says, in a tone you've never heard from her, 'I'm sorry Angie, I can't talk about it.' If you were not so dumbstruck, if you had more self respect, you might have noticed your rage just then, at her. She says she will come tomorrow to collect some of her books - ones you'd been planning to use for revision, together.

The next day you wait, insides pitching, as if your fate is still to be decided, hanging in the balance for Maddie to tip. But opening the door it's clear. Maddie's eyes avoid yours, perfunctory, and her lips are tight in disapproval - of what, you don't even question. *Maddie* is wronged, not you, that is clear. Maddie is polite and terse, with no intention of coming inside. You fetch the books from the next room - stupid not to have them by the door ready - as Maddie waits outside on the step. 'Ok, well, good luck!' she says, once she has them, indicating no amount of luck can save you, as she turns away.

◆

Outside your first exam, you and Madeleine speak as if you are casual acquaintances. She tells you about a day-trip to

London to see Michael. She's wearing an expensive dress and trainers, both new. You haven't seen her for two weeks. You feel the attention of everyone around you, as they notice the change - the strange way you're talking to each other - as if in itself this is sensational. Maddie talks about the trip blithely, the way she talked about sex with Noah, before. Where she'd gone for lunch, the money Michael spent taking her shopping after. Take it or leave it, she seems to shrug; the men are lovable suckers! You colour in the sparse account as you listen, trying not to show your desperate interest for the open wound it is: Maddie - charming, adorable, sophisticated, a girl to be awed and cowed by - so charming you'd spend any money, money you didn't have perhaps. And Maddie, there in front of you, none the worse, for seeing the deadbeat substitute for a deadbeat father, who left her years ago. *She* isn't cowed; she's stronger for it, like a vampire. You look at your old friend's big round face as she talks, thinking for the millionth time - like a puzzle you'll never grow tired of never solving: *how does it work?*

◆

You're booked to dance at a festival in Germany; Jenna has brokered one night as support on your favourite singer's tour. It's a big break, and has been a bright light in your mind for months. It's your second time abroad (Madeleine's tenth), and the two of you will dance onstage for a massive audience. You've choreographed every eventuality together; planned outfits, which other acts you'd watch, accommodation,

You and Maddie had also arranged, months ago, to travel together. Esther and your sister will go too, and your sister will drive you all to the airport, and then to the festival at the other end. But now Maddie calls to tell you she's arranged a different ride.

For a while, when you get there, it's okay. Maddie's keen to make the gig work out, and although nothing is mended, you put on a good show, hyping each other, drinking Red Stripe, smoking rolled cigarettes during breaks. Maddie is in another mode you haven't seen before. It's supposed to be different, all of this. You were supposed to figure it out together.

Of course, Maddie knows the ropes, she just doesn't leave any behind for you. There's a controlled wildness about her, supremely confident and relaxed, while you are on a precipice, unable to look at the crowd inside the huge tent, coming up with sequences on the fly to suggest to Maddie, according to the massive merged judge they form in your mind - *they'll love this* - with a feverish, desperate drive. Josh is there (avoiding you), Esther, your sister, Jenna, your promoter, backstage your musical heroes mill around like hallucinations.

After the show you immediately lose Maddie. But you've arranged to meet later, and you leave your sister, Esther and your group to cross the site to get there - and are surprised when Maddie does in fact turn up. She's towing Josh by the fingers through a crowd so tight you have to inch forward in a line with you in front - even though you have no idea where you're going. You can see

Josh is high, but you aren't sure about Maddie, who, while steering you from behind, is prattling on about Noah, as if the two of you are sitting in a coffee shop. He called her from South Africa, she says, where he was filming, to say he'd started seeing some girl he'd met. So they were having a break, Maddie explains (like Rachel and Ross!) - describing a hurtful situation as if she's in control of it. As Maddie talks, she occasionally turns back to Josh when he dances into her or wants to point something out, tugging to get her attention. They are intimate, you can see that, and you can see it is part of something larger for Maddie - her dynamic with Noah is larger, and Josh is useful for that - but they also have a special understanding. 'Josh feels really bad about what happened between us', Maddie shouts over the music into your ear. 'He wants to make it up to us - he wants us to have a good time tonight. Do you want to do some pills?'

Saying no doesn't cross your mind: Maddie is asking, holding your hand, talking in your ear, beneficent. Plus Maddie is going to do it too - and, she's doing it for *you* - for you and Maddie. The first pill Madeleine slips you does nothing. You are braced for...what? But it doesn't come. After an hour, you take a second pill, Madeleine does the same. Still nothing. An hour later, Madeleine, laughing, gives you a third, as if this is some kind of unheard of achievement - *you need three times the amount anyone else would!* For the next five hours you dance. Josh drops away somewhere. All you can see is Maddie, and sometimes others who join you, widening your circle - including at one point your sister and her friends - but they come and go. Everything and everyone is joined, there are no gaps, no silences, no stopping. Just dancing, moving, smiling, with Maddie, always there in front of you, and a graceful, wordless salvation. At dawn when the party finishes and everyone disperses, you walk back through the fields to your cabin. You don't want to disturb your sister, so you find the keys and open up the hire car, your mind in shaking fractals. Maddie sits in the driver's seat, you beside her in the passenger seat. You laugh about a couple of things - and you feel something like a sob paralyse inside you. Maddie checks her face in the rear-view mirror, says 'Oh, god,' then falls asleep. You stay awake for the hours until the festival starts coming to life again, with the sensation you're made of dried tears. The mirror on the flap in front of you stays down where you'd put it when you first got in to laugh at your appearance, and you stare at the grey face there, as if petrified by the eyes that look angry and dead at the same time.

You stay on too long after that, wanting to get the last of it. After fretting about you and your comedown, and asking you repeatedly to join her, your sister gives up on you and leaves to catch the return flight. You and Maddie stay another night, managing your states with alcohol, and wandering in and out of gentle gigs. You feel cared for, dependent, the alcohol working like a balm on your destroyed nerves - more proof of Maddie's magic knowledge. The following morning you hitch a lift with a group of kids who recognise you from the first night, riding in silence to the airport to buy another flight. Back at Maddie's place you each take a shower, and sit down with tea at the kitchen table. Maddie has already moved on, out of festival mode, into efficiency and the future - checking her mail, delighted. 'Oh my god! Haha it's here!' She opens a parcel containing a mobile phone (she's the first of your friends to have one). You watch her as she assembles it, wondering where you should go.

◆

Your opinion varies, later, according to the memories blown your way - when did it fall apart? Here? Here? *Here?* When you glance at it, the tendency is to place it at the phone call, at Madeleine's surreal non-reaction. But you do the maths one day: in a friendship that lasted no more than eighteen months, things had been good for a year, then bad for six months. And in the 'good year', when you're forensic about it, there were perhaps three months, where you could say with any veracity that you and Maddie were happy - together. You held on to each other longer, side by side as Maddie started to drift, beginning to lose faith - and you sacrificed almost everything for that brief time - for the brief faith that slipped through your hands like beads of mercury, leaving poison. It was so slight. In between Maddie's boyfriends, once, came you.

◆

You did things together after - even though you could see Maddie's callousness, the plainness that had always been there, that was somehow flourishing out in the open - you couldn't stop the pull of her, the idea of her. You felt it like a magnet, but your own field was powerless, ill fitting - without a corresponding effect. If anything, seeing her more clearly at the same time as feeling your pain increased her pull, making the paradox endlessly occupying - as if it could feed you. Maddie was gone, it was clear, but for a long time you would spend your time thinking of how to be nearer. Sometimes she would let you, and when she did, she was more out of reach than ever. You were outside, in a rank of people previously beneath you both, so far down you'd barely noticed as they dropped out of your life. But you pretended not to be broken - because how could you be, *why would you be?* You even still pretended an intimacy with Maddie, when you crossed paths; but Maddie wasn't listening. She had new words, a new language, she didn't care what you had to say.

◆

What had Maddie got out of it, you wondered. So much of it seemed to be a matter of taste or judgment - that you no longer had, or maybe never had. Your ideas and judgment *had* been important to Maddie at first (at a time when, you now realised, Maddie's hadn't meant much to you), but now they were irrelevant, discarded. Where Maddie had been a keen student, your every thought now - let alone your movements in the world - were a source of embarrassment and humiliation for you both. Your old questions came back as one existential demand: *How do I live?*

◆

You found yourself retracing the steps and stages, gathering the memories of your friendship, to explain the mystery. And you saw three Madeleines: the simplest, youngest, new-leaf Maddie you met at school - playing at being a child again; the sharper, entwined, accomplished ally of the middle; the furious, mutated stranger of the end. And those only the first in an endless list of other Madeleines - who she was now, who she was to other people; the Madeleines you never saw. There had been signs, warnings you flicked past like the irrelevant, dull pages of a book. And now some metamorphosis was complete, but you, too stupid to see it, remained inside the dark abandoned crust. Yes. How stupid you'd been, to think any of it was ordinary, taking it for granted because, like everything, it was new *(this is how you make friends, this is what real friends do, this is how you do it)*. It was like a trick, a sleight so deft you could never unpick it: *There is Maddie, plain as ever, but she causes people this (not just me!) - maybe even by telling them she can! ('Everyone falls in love with me!')* Maddie was gone, her host was no longer nutritious. You were destined to fail and fade like the portrait in the attic, while she moved on through the world, fuller, more beautiful, emboldened.

◆

For a short time, you made desultory arrangements now and then, and sometimes bumped into each other in the street. Maddie would reach out to draw you in then, effusive - but it was an image of something gone, a muscle memory, unsatisfying for both of you.

A night out with some of Maddie's new friends, where Maddie danced in a way you didn't recognise, and you did coke together in the toilet, Maddie and her friend laughing at private jokes while you decided to go home early.

On results day, your mother went into school to read your grades - straight As - posted on the wall, because you'd started a summer job as an assistant at a TV production company. The following week, running into each other at the pub at your old favourite night, Madeleine laughed at your grades and your job - 'So typical!', she said, telling you about her Bs and a C, and how she was working in a karaoke bar for the summer; how Noah would collect her every night and serenade her with her favourite tracks. You didn't tell her there was nothing to your job - the people were lifeless and your role was indiscernible; every moment painful. She was saying she was mediocre, and that you were excelling. You were thinking: *she's got it right. She's still doing it better.*

A lunch outside, where Maddie spilled her drink on her jeans and ran, laughing into the loos with her shopping bag from that morning, emerging (in the kind of tiny, striped mini dress that would look awful on you), beaming. Some guy at a table of men next to you saying 'That was handy!' and they all laughed - signalling their superiority to this loud, vain girl, to cover their leering.

Esther reports seeing Maddie in a bar, with Noah and

a group of their friends. 'You know how she's an actress - I was thinking, she was *always acting* - and her clothes are completely different, she was wearing this pencil skirt and fitted top - her new part is obviously Sexy Secretary!'

A letter, which you read as if it might give you the answer, but which was too late to mean anything. She'd written it when you stopped seeing each other, but hadn't sent it for months - it was full of dead affection, and no information at all. It was plain, like Maddie, so plain that its outsized effect on you added to what seemed by then like witchcraft.

Messages, on special occasions for a couple of years; New Year's Eve, birthdays. Tiny lapses; wormholes to an old affection.

A phone call, when Maddie wanted you to know she was getting married. A persistent sense you had, of having fallen; not just of not knowing what to do, or how to live, but of *doing it wrong*.

A dream. You're walking alone down the high street (in a part of town you hate) and the music is everywhere - in the world but from your mind. *Every time it rains.* You know this feeling as if from another self in another life - vibrating from requited love, like a baby - but not why you have it. Then *there she is*, walking towards you - happy!, to see you - and the sight of her is also an answer: *So that's why I feel like this.*

A boyfriend picking up a photograph, never framed or discarded. 'Wow, who's that?! It's intense.' In it, Maddie, standing square on, looks into the camera. The luminous plains of her Mona Lisa face and her shoulders in a denim jacket fill the frame. She wears no makeup and her eyes are wide. Everything, it seems, is bare, nothing is posed. You can see she's looking at someone she trusts, who is, possibly, under her control but also misbehaving - in her glance is the tiniest hint of intimacy, like a shared joke. Michael had taken it. Near the end, for them, but before you met. When you first saw it, similarly disregarded in Maddie's bedroom, you'd complimented her on it. 'Do you want it?' Maddie had asked, immediately. 'Take it.'

Thoughts, rarer and rarer. Months and sometimes whole years; nothing.

◆

And later, you think, when you do think about it - you have neat thoughts like: it's because of what happened when you were small. You needed someone, and Madeleine did too, for a time, but she also needed more, and more, and more. But that's not right, is it? It can't be reduced like that.

And even here, you leave out so much. All your ugliness, really - your guilt, your anger - terrifying to everyone - just like your father. How would Maddie tell this? It might just be that you didn't know her. It might be that she was a phoney. It might be that you were. Stories are phoney.

◆

When Maddie showed up in my dreams after, I didn't know that dreams aren't just from our minds, they're *of* them - that everything in the dream was me: the street, the music, Maddie, the feeling. As I woke, and it drained from me like a life force, I didn't yet know that the feeling didn't belong to her; I couldn't know that the dream said it was possible, because it was there before Maddie and would be after. That it began with my mother, then my father; that I would recognise it within minutes of meeting someone; that my children and their children would summon it over and over as if it were trivial.

◆

I used to wish I could draw a line - I tried to make sense of it, like this. There's satisfaction and torture, necessity and failure in making a story - in forcing one. I realised, it's beyond my control. The truths are in the fragments, that will always come and go (along with the others - all the involuntary ones, like sliding down the bannister of the house where I was born, or watching the skin form on the milk my mother's heating for me as I sit where she's balanced me on the brown counter; prickles of shame; a swarm of bliss; a blue line; a dream) and in listening to the fragments, to the attempts at story and to when they arrive. I sometimes think of myself as an organ, that's been pushed and stroked and beaten and adored - and these things, all these things remain.

Madeleine

Acknowledgements

Thank you to Sam Ruddock and Julia Webb for finding 'Madeleine' in the pile - and to Sam for unstinting, generous encouragement and razor-sharp editing.

Thank you to my first and beloved reader Rebecca Ascher Walsh.

Thank you to my early and constant readers and friends in the WC, Rod McLaren and Celia Romaniuk.

Thank you to Phil Baines and Catherine Dixon for the cover of my dreams.

Thank you to my beautiful family.

Thank you for supporting planet-friendly publishing

Story Machine seeks to have a net positive social and environmental impact. That means the environment and people's lives are actually better off for every book we print. Story Machine offsets our entire carbon footprint plus 10% through a www.ClimateCare.org programme. We are now investing in converting to use only 100% renewable energies and seeking out the most planet-positive means of shipping books to our readers.

The printing insustry is a huge polluter, requiring the use of huge amounts of water, toxic chemicals, and energy. Even FSC certified mix paper sources drive deforestation. That's why we are proud to be working with www.Seacort.net, a global leader in planet positive printing. Not only have they developed a waterless and chemical-free process, they use only 100% renewable energies, FSC certified recycled paper, and direct absolutely no waste to landfill. That's why they were crowned Europe's most sustainable SME in 2017, and have been recognised as one of the top three environmental printers in the world.

Planet-positive printing costs us a little more. But we think this is a small price to pay for a better world, today and in the future. If you agree, please share our message, and encourage other publishers and authors to commit to planet-positive printing. Stories can change the world. They deserve publishers that want to make sure they do. Together, we can make publishing more sustainable.